Uppercase Fun

Big Bird loves learning the ABCs!
The big letters in the alphabet are
called **uppercase** letters. The small
letters are called **lowercase** letters.

  Say the name of each letter.
Then trace all of the letters.

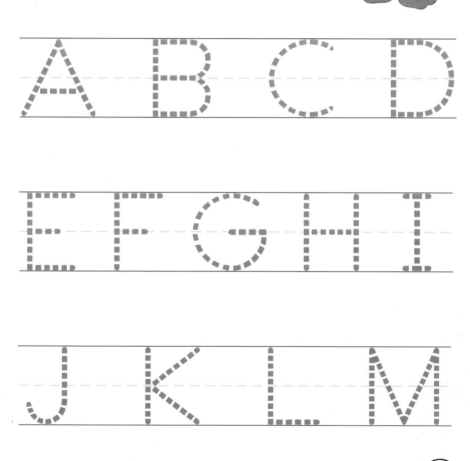

GROVER

  Say the name of each letter.
Then trace all of the letters.

N O P Q R

S T U V

W X Y Z

Lowercase Fun

  Say the name of each picture.
Then trace the letter.

a b c

d e f g h i

j k l m n

Say the name of each letter.
Then trace all of the letters.

o p q r s t

u v w x y z

Each **uppercase** letter has
a **lowercase** partner.

 Say the letter names.

 Then draw a line to match each
uppercase letter to its **lowercase** partner.

 G

 **egg**

 **A**

 carrot

 E

 apple

 B

 **grapes**

 C

 banana

Help Cookie Monster and Prairie Dawn go from **Aa** to **Zz**.

Draw a line through the path that shows the correct letter partners.

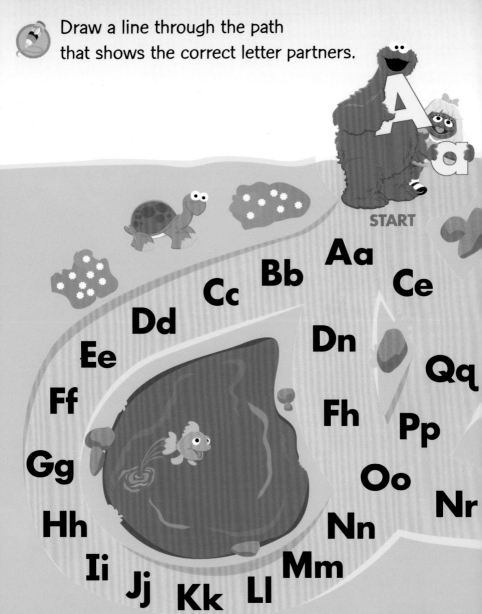

START

Aa

Bb

Cc

Ce

Dd

Dn

Ee

Ff

Qq

Fh

Pp

Gg

Oo

Nr

Hh

Nn

Ii Jj Kk Ll Mm

Ek Zz Lj Yg

Uu Vv Ww

Rr Ss Tt Tr Xx

Xf Yy

Ym Zz

Zc

Og

Tv

Xu Pw

FINISH

Fun With Letters SESAME STREET

Say the name of each letter you see.
Color the spaces using the color key.

Color Key

A=   B=   C=   D=   E=   F=

 Say the name of each picture.

 Draw a line from each picture to the letter that stands for its beginning sound.

 •

•J

 •

•R

 •

•W

 •

•L

 •

•S

 •

•E

 •

•A

 •

•D

 •

•B

 •

•Q

q

Draw a line from each **uppercase** letter to the matching **lowercase** letter.

Say the name of each letter you see.

 Color the spaces using the color key.

Color Key

W =   X =   Y =   Z =

Come join the party!

 Color all of the balloons with **uppercase** letters.

Letter Tic Tac Toe

Help Cookie Monster find the objects
that begin with the same letter!

 Write the beginning letter
next to each picture.

 Draw an **X** over the three pictures
that begin with the same letter.

Short Vowel Fun

Big Bird has so much fun learning
about the short **a**, **e**, **i**, **o**, and **u** sounds!

 Say the name of each picture.

| hat | bed | fish | frog | tub |

Draw a line from each picture to the letter
that stands for its middle sound.

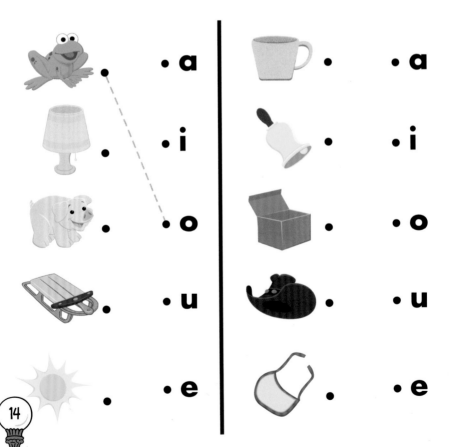

Long Vowel Fun

Big Bird knows all of the long **a**, **e**, **i**, **o**, and **u** sounds!

a e i o u

 Say the name of each picture.

pail	leaf	kite	boat	suit

Draw a line from each picture to the letter that stands for its middle sound. Look at the pictures in the box if you need help.

• **a**

• **e**

• **i**

• **o**

• **u**

GLUE

• **a**

• **e**

• **i**

• **o**

• **u**

15

What letter is at the beginning of your name?
Practice writing your name below. Then draw
a picture of something that starts with the same
letter as your name.